M. J. GROVER

Rockhounding on the Pacific Northwest Coast

The Best Beaches to find agates, jaspers and fossils

For more rockhounding adventures, go to agatehunting.com

First edition

ISBN: 978-1-7362750-4-7

This book was professionally typeset on Reedsy.
Find out more at reedsy.com

Contents

Agates, Jaspers & So Much More...

The beaches of the Pacific Northwest have a wide array of beautiful treasures just waiting to be discovered. In this book, we are going to take a detailed look at the best sites for rockhounding in Washington, Oregon and Northern California. But first, we should get a better idea of just what exactly we should be on the lookout for!

Agate

Agates are a type of chalcedony, a microcrystalline form of silica. They are formed when volcanic ash or sediment is exposed to extreme high heat and pressure over time. These agate generally form as nodules within the cracks and voids of a volcanic rock.

The result is a beautiful unique mineral that can feature intricate banding, unique patterns and vibrant colors. Agates come in a wide array of colors, including clear, yellow, orange, red, brown, blue, green, and even black. They are translucent stones that will brighten up when light passes through them.

Agates may start out jagged and rough textured when they are found close to the source. By the time they turn up on the beach, they have usually worn smooth and round after a great amount of erosion and weathering.

For most Pacific Northwest rockhounds, agates are the main prize.

Jasper

Jasper is a type of opaque, fine-grained, impure variety of quartz that is found in many different colors and patterns. It is composed of chalcedony and microcrystalline quartz and is characterized by its strong, solid color and swirling patterns.

The composition of jasper is nearly identical to agates as it forms in the exact same environment. The one exception is that the silica gel is exposed to some impurity, resulting in the formation of an opaque jasper. Unlike an agate, jasper material will not allow light to pass through it.

Jasper is abundant all along the Pacific Coast and throughout Puget Sound. It comes in many different colors and patterns, including red, yellow, brown, green, blue, and black.

Jasp-Agate

Be on the lookout for jasp–agates while exploring the gravel beds. These are simply stones that have characteristics of both agate and jasper mixed together in one stone.

Some of by best pieces are actually jasp-agate. The swirling mixture of agate matrix in rich opaque jasper can be absolutely stunning.

Orbicular Jasper

Be on the lookout for orbicular jaspers while walking the beach. While I'm sure they could be found anywhere on the Pacific shoreline, they are most commonly found in Washington state. These beautiful stones are identified by their distinctive sphere, or "orb" patterns throughout the stone.

In Washington they are most commonly black, grey, and dark red, though they can sometimes be found in different color varieties.

Polishing orbicular jaspers can be a nice enhancement, as the brighter finish can really help to accentuate the amazing patterns.

Sea Glass

Sea glass is a type of naturally weathered glass that has been smoothed and rounded over time by the action of waves and sand in the ocean. It is found along coastal shores and high quality pieces are highly prized by collectors for its unique color and texture.

Sea glass is created when broken pieces of glass, such as bottle fragments or shattered windows, are thrown into the ocean and tumbled by the waves over many years. The rough edges of the glass are worn down and the surface is polished, creating a smooth and frosted appearance.

The glass will retain its original color, so clear, green and "beer bottle browns" are more common and perhaps less desirable. The real treasures are the dark blues, reds and purples. For some collectors, sea glass is their main target.

Sea glass can potentially be found anywhere, but there are a few select beaches that are well-known for their abundant sea glass. We have highlighted some of them in this book.

Petrified Wood

Petrified wood forms when trees fall into swamps, rivers, or lakes and are buried by sediment. Over time, minerals in the water percolate through the wood and replace the organic material, preserving the structure and texture of the original wood.

The process can take millions of years, and the result is a stunning stone that features the natural grain and texture of the wood, as well as the vibrant colors and patterns created by the minerals.

Petrified wood can come in all sizes. Most pieces you will find on the beach has spent a great amount of time rolling around in the ocean, so smaller stone fragments are most common. Keep a sharp eye out for the telltale sign of tree rings in the stone. For beginners it can sometimes be challenging to identify petrified wood. If you have any doubt, bring it home and ask an experienced collector for help.

Fossils

The beaches of Oregon, Washington and Northern California can turn up a wide variety of fossils; plant fossils, vertebrates and invertebrates.

Vertebrates are anything that has a skeleton. These are much rarer, and due to their value to science, the collection of vertebrate fossils requires a permit.

However, invertebrate and plant fossils, which you are much more likely to encounter, can legally be collected.

Some examples of these fossils include:

- clams
- scallops
- crabs
- oysters
- crinoids
- mollusks
- shrimp

They can usually be identified easily because they will have a rock matrix attached to them. In some areas (particularly within the Astoria Formation of the Central Oregon Coast) fossils are abundant and even more common than agates or jaspers.

Also be on the lookout for unusually round rocks. These are sedimentary rocks called "concretions," and they often form around fossils. These can be spherical or disc shaped. Sometimes you can crack them open with a rock hammer and expose fossils inside. Most will be empty, but sometimes you will be greeted with a nice surprise!

Glass Fishing Floats

It is now quite rare to find a true Japanese glass fishing float. These were round glass balls used by fishermen throughout history to keep their fishing nets or longlines afloat. Sometimes they would come loose from the nets and float all the way across the Pacific Ocean and show up on our shores. The ones found on the Pacific Coast likely originate from Japan or other East Asian countries.

Modern fishing floats have mostly been replaced by styrofoam and plastic, which means that any clear glass float is likely many decades old. While most floats have long ago made their way across the ocean and been found, it is believed that many are still out there trapped in circular ocean currents. On occasion these antique floats still find their way across.

Today, glass fishing floats are highly prized by collectors for their historical significance and decorative appeal, and are used for a variety of decorative purposes, such as for decorating beach houses or for use as lawn ornaments.

There are a few towns along the coast that hide modern glass floats to encourage tourism. Unlike the antique floats, these modern floats are colorful art pieces made by skilled glass blowers.

"Pretty Rocks"

Most of the rocks that you will find along the shores of the Pacific Ocean and Puget Sound will not be all that exciting. They will be a mix of glacial till from various sandstone, shale, limestone, basalt, granite, etc.

While there are thousands of different types of minerals, it is a few dozen rock types that make up the vast majority of what can be found along the Pacific Coast. While it may not be important to identify and differentiate these different types, there's nothing wrong with seeking them out and adding them to your collection.

That is the great thing about rockhounding. You get to decide which rocks to keep and which to toss back. If you like it, then by all means add it to your collection!

Successful Rockhounding Tips

Here are a few tips to help you be successful on your next rockhounding adventure:

- **Research the locations:** You have this book so you already have an advantage here! There are hundreds of miles of coastline in the Pacific Northwest and not all of it is good for rockhounding. Most areas are sandy and unproductive most of the time. Seek out locations that have a good reputation as productive rockhounding sites.

- **Hunt at low tide:** The high tide brings agates and other rocks up onto the beach. As the tide lowers it leaves them exposed for you to find.

- **Look for gravel:** It is so important to look for areas that have gravel beds exposed on the beach. There are some beaches that are great places for beachcombing, but if everything is covered with sand then you aren't going to have any luck. The beach can look different with each tide. Keep an eye out for exposed gravel and get out there and start hunting when you see it. This is when you will find all those nice agates and jaspers.

- **Look for color:** This will probably come quite naturally, but be on the lookout for anything that "stands out" from the rocks around it. Most beaches will be comprised of similar type of rock such as basalt, granite, etc. A nice red jasper or a shiny clear agate should stick out among the more common rocks.

- **Check creeks and rivers:** Sometimes the beaches just aren't cooperating. Rockhounding along the Pacific Coast is best during the winter months, and for much of the years all that you will find is miles and miles of sand. In these instances, some of the best places to hunt will be at the mouth of small creeks and rivers where they flow into the ocean. Hunting these areas can be productive when nowhere else is.

- **Look for patterns:** Keep your eye out for stones with unusual patterns. Dark colored agates might go unnoticed if not for their banding and orb patterns. Parallel lines on petrified wood specimens might be the only thing that distinguishes it from other common stones.

- **Use a scoop:** Some of us aren't as young as we use to be. A small scoop on the end of a long handle can prevent us from having to bend over hundreds of times. After a long day this can be a real lifesaver. A bent spoon duct-taped on the end of a dowel is a cheap, effective homemade scoop that can make rockhounding a lot more fun.

- **Walk toward the sun:** This is a great way to spot agates that others have missed. Don't hunt with the sun to your back. Instead, wear a hat to shield your eyes from the sun and look *toward the sun.* What you will realize is that agates will absolutely glow! I can spot a marble-sized agate from 20 feet away if the sun is shining through it just right.

- **Sit and dig:** This isn't my preferred method, but lots of people have success just sitting down and sifting through a thick gravel bed. I think this is a better option for folks who don't have great vision and need a closer look at the rocks. It definitely works, and you'll also find a lot of smaller pieces that you just don't notice when you are walking and covering ground.

- **Join a club:** With the guidance of this book you shouldn't have any trouble finding some nice rocks to add to your collection, but that doesn't mean that you wouldn't benefit from joining a rockhounding club. There are lots of clubs all throughout the Pacific Northwest, and its a great way to meet others with similar interests and explore new rockhounding areas.

- **Go in the winter:** While you can certainly go beachcombing anytime of year, you'll have the best luck between November and April. The nasty weather and big waves that come along with that winter weather helps to strip away sand from the beach and expose gravel beds.

Rockhounding Rules and Ethics

Good rockhounds follow a strict code of ethics to ensure that our hobby remains sustainable and looked at in a positive light. Collecting rocks is a fun family activity. Be a good steward of the land and ensure that we can continue to enjoy this hobby for generations to come.

Rockhounder's Code of Ethics

1. **Obtain permission:** Before rock collecting on private property, always obtain the owner's permission.
2. **Respect protected areas:** Rock collecting is not allowed in designated wilderness areas, national parks, and many other protected lands.
3. **Follow beach access rules:** Check with local authorities to determine the rules for accessing and collecting rocks on public beaches. Some beaches may be restricted during certain times of the year, such as during bird nesting season.
4. **Follow all posted regulations:** Many of the sites in this book are within city, county and state parks. Always read the posted regulations follow any rules or restrictions.
5. **Limit your collecting:** Some areas may have restrictions on the amount of rocks you can collect, so be sure to check with the appropriate agency. General etiquette would be to collect a modest amount and leave plenty of rocks for others.
6. **Respect wildlife:** Be mindful not disturb wildlife, such as birds or marine

life, or damage their habitats.

7. **Personal use:** Rocks that you collect should be for personal use. Do not collect with the intent to sell.

8. **Fill all holes:** If you do any digging, limit yourself to small holes that you can easily fill in at the end of the day. Always leave the area as good as you found it.

9. **Pick up trash:** Always pack out trash that you create, and consider picking up a few other pieces to help keep our beaches clean.

10. **Be a good person:** Overall, conduct yourself in a manner that ensures that rockhounding is looked at in a positive light.

Washington Coast Rockhounding Rules

In Washington, the rules and regulations about rockhounding on beaches will vary depending on the specific location and jurisdiction. There are city parks, county parks, state parks, private lands, national parks, Indian reservations and other land designations along the Pacific Coast and throughout Puget Sound.

Most of the Washington sites covered in this book are county and state parks. I could find very little mention of any rules about collecting rocks here. People have been collecting here forever and I've never heard of anyone getting into trouble.

A few of these sites are within Indian Reservations. Again, I couldn't find any official rules regarding rockhounding on tribal lands. If you are respectful and following the general rules as a visitor on their lands then I doubt you'll have any issue with casual collecting.

I mention a few beaches in this book that are within the Olympic National Park.

Rockhounding within the National Park System is generally prohibited.

NOTE: Many of the beaches are Washington State Parks. You will need to purchase a Discovery Pass to use these sites, including day-use parking. At the time of this writing an annual pass costs $35, and gives you access to millions of acres of state recreation lands. The pass is transferable between two vehicles, and expires 1-year from the date of purchase.

Oregon Coast Rockhounding Rules

The entire 363-mile stretch of the Oregon Coast is a state park. This means that the public has access to every inch of the Oregon Coast!

Agates, jasper, seashells, driftwood, invertebrate fossils, and other non-living items can be legally collected on the Oregon Coast, with a few simple rules:

1. Collected items cannot be sold and must be for personal use only.
2. The total collected material is limited to 1-gallon per day, 3 gallons per year.
3. Collected sand is limited to 5-gallons per day, 20 gallons per year.
4. Collected cobble is limited to 5-gallons per day, 10 gallons per year.
5. Collected driftwood is limited to one cubic yard per day, 3 cord per year.
6. The state reserves the right to limit collecting of natural materials within certain areas if deemed necessary to protect resources.

Casual collecting of agates, fossils, driftwood and other treasures along the coast is encouraged and welcomed as a boon to the local economy.

Northern California

The rules and regulations regarding rock collecting on the California Coast can vary depending on the specific location. In general, you are allowed to collect rocks and other minerals from public beaches along the Pacific Coast of California.

Some beaches in Northern California are privately owned and inaccessible to the public. The California Coastal Act acknowledges that public access begins where sand is wet (below the high tide line).

As with most other states, California allows rock collecting on the beaches of the Pacific Ocean with some limitations.

1. Rocks cannot be sold commercially or collected with the intent to profit.
2. One person cannot take more than 15 pounds of mineralogical material, or not more than one specimen over 15 pounds.
3. Tools cannot be used for the extraction of mineralogical material.

In this book, we will focus on highlighting only a few of the best Northern California beaches that provide public access and allow legal rockhounding.

Please remember, while we have gone to great lengths to research the legalities of rockhounding on the Pacific Coast, it is ultimately the readers responsibility to ensure that you are within the boundaries of the law.

While I personally have not experienced any issues with casual rockhounding or beachcombing, be aware that laws can change at any time. When in doubt, do your own research and make your own decisions.

Navigating to these Sites

The standard format for most guide books over the years is to give detailed directions to each site with specific details about every twist and turn along the way.

In the 2020s and beyond, I highly doubt that people make use of details like that. These sites aren't deep in the woods.

Since the Pacific Coast is so popular for tourism, most of the sites in this book have good signage and paved roads leading right to the beach. Many of the accesses are county and state parks. You won't need a 4-wheel drive vehicle or any special equipment to navigate to them.

To pack as many good sites as possible into this book, I have opted not to waste a lot of space telling you to "go 1/2 a mile, look for a red barn, turn right, etc. etc. etc."

All of the locations in this book should be easy to find by putting the specific beach name into your smartphone. The beginning of each chapter has a map showing the general location of the sites and the nearby towns.

For a few sites that are less well-known, I have included specific details to help you get there. Overall, I'm confident that finding these sites won't be a problem for you.

1. Bellingham Area

Semiahmoo Spit

This site is a nice day-use access managed by Whatcom County Parks and Rec. You'll find larger gravel and cobble at this site. There is public access to both sides of the spit, but the better material will likely be found on the west side that faces the Strait of Georgia.

Birch Bay State Park

Birch Bay State Park provides over 1.5 miles of rocky shoreline for beach-combers. This is a great place to search for beautiful Whatcom County agates, as well as the occasional jasper, sea shells and sea glass. Aside from rockhounding on the beach, there are a wide array of family fun activities. There are 147 camping sites available.

Cherry Point

One of the overlooked beaches in this area is at Cherry Point. There's no signs to get here, and you'll encounter way less people than most other sites. A nice rocky shoreline extends of miles, with big round colorful rocks.

One note to access. The best parking access is about a mile to the southeast of where Cherry Point is marked on most maps. Head east on Henry Road for about 3/4 mile, then turn south at Gulf Road. On maps, there is a "derelict conveyor" marked right at the parking area.

Sunset Beach

You'll have to take the small ferry to Lummi Island to access this beach. Check online for the ferry schedule. Enjoy about 800 feet of rocky beach adjacent to Rosario Strait. This is a known agate hunting site, but the extra effort required to get here means the beach is less likely to be picked over than other sites.

2. Fidalgo Island

There isn't a lot of beach access on Fidalgo Island, but one standout site for rockhounding is Rosario Beach. It falls within the Deception Pass State Park.

Rosario Beach

This is a popular rockhounding location near the town of Anacortes. There are actually two easily accessible beaches here, one on either side of a peninsula. Park at the Rosario Head Trailhead and head toward the beach. To your right is Rosario Beach, to your left is Sharpe Cove. Both spots are fun to hunt.

If you want, you can take a short hike east on the Pacific NW Trail for several thousand more feet of rocky shoreline to search.

Walking along the shore, you can't help but bend down to see the colorful rocks that litter the shores. The color varieties found here will rival any beach on the coast. While you should certainly keep your eyes peeled for agates and jaspers, you are likely to be just as mesmerized by the beautiful variety of the more "average" rocks at this site.

This beach can get busy in the summertime. Deception Pass is the most visited state park in Washington. Visit during the winter (when rockhounding is best anyways) and it will be much less crowded.

3. San Juan Islands

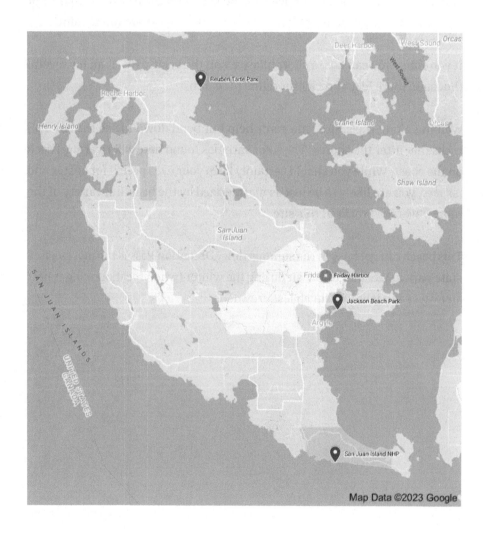

San Juan Island is known for its diverse natural beauty, including miles of rugged coastline, pristine beaches, and rolling hills. It is truly one of the hidden gems of Washington state.

The shores of San Juan Island have long been a destination for beachcombers. While it certainly takes some effort to get here, there are miles and miles of beaches that you can explore to your hearts desire. Get here via ferry access to Friday Harbor.

There are many parks along the shores of San Juan Island, but many of them have too many cliffs to make for good rockhounding.

Ruben Tarte County Park

This is a small county park on the north end of the island. This isn't the biggest site, but there are a few hundred feet of gravel shoreline that to explore.

Jackson Beach State Park

There are lots of rocks and driftwood at Jackson Beach Park near Argyle. Access to this site is very easy with a road following right along the beach. There are several thousand feet of shoreline for beachcombers. If you like driftwood, this is an excellent site for you.

San Juan Island National Historic Park

This is the standout access on the southern tip of San Juan Island. If you are making the trip to the island to try and find agates, they you definitely want to come here and go for a hunt.

There are miles and miles to explore, and almost all of it is good for rock-hounding.

On the north end of the park, check out Fourth of July Beach and Jakle's Beach Lagoon. On the south end, explore the long gravel beach of South Beach. This is a fantastic agate hunting site.

4. Lopez Island

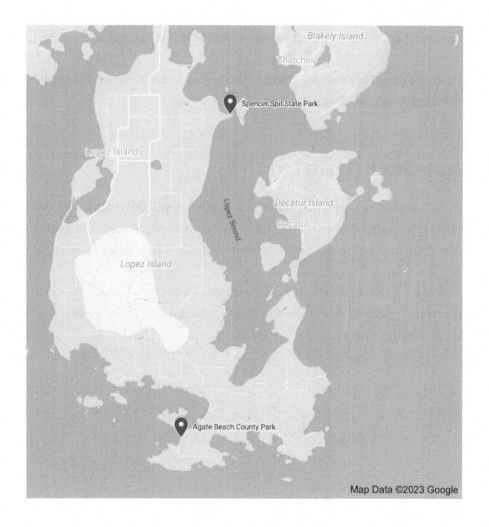

Access Lopez Island by taking the ferry from Fidalgo Island near Anacortes. The Island has a handful of public access points to beaches around the island. The two highlighted below are the best for rockhounding.

Spencer Spit State Park

This park includes the unusual triangle shaped Spencer Spit that juts out eastward toward Frost Island. You'll find rich deposits of agates, jasper, and other types of rocks. Visitors can find these unique and beautiful rocks along the shoreline, among the rocks and boulders that line the beach.

There are camping sites available and this is a popular site for kayaking when the wind is agreeable.

Agate Beach County Park

It's a steep hike to get down to this beach, but you will be rewarded for your efforts. With the combination of ferry access and being on the south side of the island, this site doesn't get too many visitors. Mostly locals at this site.

Lots of smooth round rocks to explore at this site. If you are looking to get off the beaten path and away from the crowds, give this park a try. I think you'll be pleasantly surprised.

5. Whidbey Island

Whidbey Island is a perhaps the most popular agate hunting location in all of Washington. It's a relatively short drive from the Seattle metro area, and has many public beaches that provide access to rocky shorelines. Agates are plentiful if you are there at the right time.

Deception Pass

Deception Pass is Washington's most visited state parks for good reason. The park's rugged shoreline and tide pools are exceedingly beautiful. It's also home to a rich variety of rocks, including agates, jasper, petrified wood, and other types of stones. Visitors can find these beautiful and unique rocks along the shoreline and among the rocks and boulders that line the beach. Focus your efforts on the gravel shores west of the bridge at North Beach and West Beach for the best odds.

Hyde Beach

This is a nice access a few miles south of Deception Pass, right next to the Naval Air Station. This is a small access with about 10 parking spots, but it doesn't get near as many visitors as other sites. It provides decent access for rocky shores of Whidbey Island.

Joseph Whidbey State Park

This is a great access with nice views of Lopez Island and the Strait of Juan de Fuca. You'll have no shortage of rocks to sort through at this site. With 3,100 feet of shoreline covered with the normal granites, conglomerates, and serpentine rocks, spend enough time here and you are certain to find the lovely agates that Whidbey Island is famous for.

Fort Ebey State Park

This site is an old coastal defense fort built during World War 2. Now it is one of the most popular public accesses on Whidbey Island.

For rockhounds this site is hard to beat. It has over 3-miles of saltwater shoreline to explore with abundant rocks. Be careful of the tall bluffs along the shoreline. They are constantly eroding and can be dangerous to stand directly under.

There is plenty of hiking, fishing, picnicking and camping at this site.

Ebey's Landing National Historic Reserve

This is another great access with several miles of rocky shoreline to explore. Between Ebey's Landing and Fort Ebey State Park, you should have no difficulty finding lots of treasures for your rock collection.

Fort Casey Historical State Park

You can park at the main parking lot at Fort Casey Beach where the ferry leave for Port Townsend. The Keystone Spit separates Crockett Lake from Puget Sound. You'll have over 2 miles of rocky shoreline to explore.

Ledgewood Beach County Park

An overlooked beach on Whidbey Island. This is a much smaller access than most, but it's the perfect site if you prefer to avoid crowds.

Lagoon Point County Park

Another small, beautiful access that provides plenty of rocky shoreline to explore. Great site for driftwood, and plenty of agates to be found if you put in the effort.

South Whidbey State Park

This park gets more attention for its rare old-grown stands of douglas fir, spruce, western hemlock and red cedar trees. There are lots of camping sites and hiking trails. To access the beach, take the 0.3 mile long Beach Trail down to the water and you will have 4,500 feet of gravel beach to explore.

Double Bluff County Park

This is a dog-friendly beach, so it is fairly popular with the locals and the small parking lot can fill quickly. Lots of driftwood and seashells at this site. Walk west toward the bluffs and you should start getting into better gravel which will turn up agates, jaspers and other nice interesting rocks to put in your rock tumbler.

Possession Beach Waterfront Park

You'll have to hike a fairly steep trail to get to the beach at this site. Not for the faint of heart, but if you're willing to put in the effort you will be rewarded with a nice quiet beach which receives fewer visitors than just about any other public access on the island.

6. Camano Island

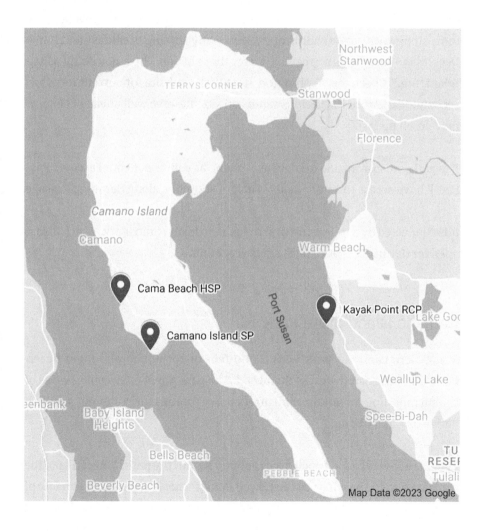

Situated about 1 hour north of Seattle, Camano Island is a great site for beachcombing. Unfortunately, the beaches on the island are mostly private property. There are two large parks on the southwest side of the island that provide the best access for the public.

Cama Beach Historical State Park

Cama Beach started as a family fishing resort back in the 1930s. There are no campsites at this park, but there are 33 cabins on site that area available for rent, along with a cafe that is open seasonally serving breakfast and lunch. Needless to say, this is a great option for those of you who enjoy doing a little "glamping." Check the Washington State Parks website for current rates and accommodations of the various cabins on site. Reserve well ahead of time, as they do fill up fast.

The park is also available for day-use as long as you've got your Discover Pass. You'll have access to a mile-and-a-half of shoreline along Saratoga Passage.

It is connected by a mile-long trail to Camano Island State Park, which also is open for day use and overnight stays year 'round.

Camano Island State Park

A 244-acre camping park with 6,700 feet of rocky shoreline and beach, located 14 miles southwest of Stanwood. The park provides sweeping views of the surrounding mountains and offers opportunities for crabbing, shellfish harvesting and hiking.

There are several good beach access points within the park. You can take the trail down to the beach from the Lowell Point Picnic Area on the north end of the park, or go to the main parking area by the boat ramp. Other small parking areas have short trails down to the rocky shoreline.

Kayak Point Regional County Park

This one is actually a short 25-minute drive north of Everett. Not technically on Camano Island, its a convenient site to for beachcombers in the area. It provides 3,300 feet of rocky shoreline for beachcombing. This is a great site if you want to get out of the Seattle Metro area but still a relatively easy drive.

7. Seattle Area

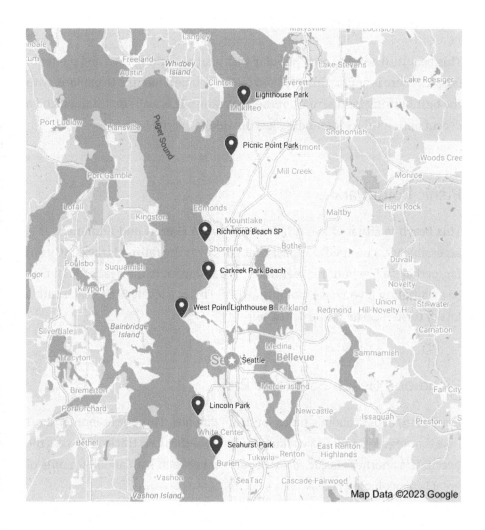

I generally seek out more secluded areas, so the beaches in the Seattle Metro area certainly would not be my first choices for beachcombing. With that said, there are plenty of good opportunities if you are looking for an area close to home. Expect lots of company at these sites. Use caution by keeping valuables hidden out of sight to prevent broken windows in the parking area. This can be a problem anywhere, but it's particularly worth noting for sites closer to the city.

Mukilteo Lighthouse Park

This beautiful beach is very popular with a large parking area and plenty of people. There is approximately 1500 feet or cobble shoreline to explore, with the best hunting being south of the boat ramp. It is well-maintained and a decent option for rockhounding just outside of Everett.

Picnic Point Park

This beach is situated about halfway between Everett and Edmonds. It is accessible via a ramped overpass that goes over the railroad tracks. It's not far, perhaps a few hundred feet from the parking lot to the beach, but it may be a limitation if you have mobility issues. This is a lovely little beach with a lots of rocks, seashells and driftwood.

Richmond Beach Saltwater Park

Here's a great park about 4 miles south of Edmonds. This one is another short hike that requires taking a walking bridge over the train tracks to access the beach. It's another classic rocky Puget Sound beach with about 3/4 mile of great beachcombing access.

Carkeek Park Beach

This 220-acre park is situated just north of Seattle and is one of the states most popular parks. Standing on the beach, it would be easy to forget that you are surrounded by a major metro area. It's popular enough that you should expect plenty of company, but the beach is still worth a visit.

West Point Lighthouse Beach

Discovery Park is another very popular park just outside of Seattle. Drive through the park on Discovery Park Road to access shoreline at Discovery Park Beach (south side of the lighthouse) or West Point Lighthouse Beach (north side of the lighthouse). Each beach offers about 1/2 mile of rocky shore.

Lincoln Park

A good pebbly beach in the heart of the city. This is a truly multi-use park with hiking trails, athletic fields and even a heated saltwater swimming pool. For beachcombers, there is a 1-mile long paved path that follows right along the shores of Puget Sound. Needless to say, you can expect company here, but you might be able to find a few good rocks here nonetheless.

Seahurst Park

This is a beautiful park about 2 miles northwest of Burien. As with the other parks in the Seattle metro area you can expect plenty of fellow beachcombers. Another nice beach with a nice variety of rocks and driftwood.

8. Tacoma Area

Titlow Beach

I wouldn't necessarily seek out Titlow Beach, but it is still a decent option for rockhounding if you live in the Tacoma area and don't want to travel very far.

Owen's Beach

You can definitely find some nice rocks and driftwood at Owen's Beach, but expect some company! This beach gets lots of visitors, but exploring the beach during the winter months will likely improve your experience.

Fox Island Sand Spit

Beaches on Fox Island have long been known to produce nice agates. Usually smaller in size, they can be plentiful if you time your visit right. The very northernmost point of the island is the Fox Island Sand Spit (part of the Tacoma DeMolay Sandspit Nature Preserve). This is my favorite beach in the Tacoma area.

Saltar's Point Beach

This is another awesome little pebble beach that is about a 30 minute drive from Tacoma. Search at low tide and you've got good odds of finding an agate here. The parking area is small. Take a small walking bridge over the train tracks to access the beach.

9. Bremerton Area

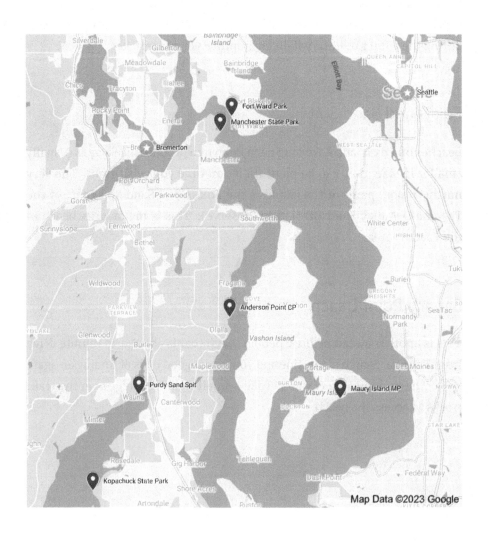

Kopachuck State Park

If encountered more sand dollars here than anywhere in Washington. Lots of other shells, crabs and other marine critters too, along with a few jaspers and the occasional agate to keep you busy.

Purdy Sand Spit

This great little access is just north of Gig Harbor. Park at the Purdy Boat Launch or at the wide parking pullouts along the main road. This isn't the most peaceful beach due to the main road running right along the beach, but its an easy access and never fails to turn up some interesting finds for beachcombers.

Anderson Point County Park

There's about a 15 minute hike from the parking area down to the beach. I love it because it means this beach gets a lot less visitors than many surrounding areas, but this may be limiting for you if the hike is an issue. There's a decent elevation drop down to the beach. Often you will be rewarded with nice pebbly beach that you have all to yourself.

Manchester State Park

I haven't found anything exceptional at Manchester Park, but if you're in Bremerton it's the closest option to hunt a gravel shoreline. This beach certainly has potential and I have no doubt it will turn up something nice if you are there at the right time.

Fort Ward State Park

It's only a few miles "as the crow flies" but it will take about an hour from Bremerton to drive over to Bainbridge Island and down to Fort Ward State Park. It's worth the drive, as you will be greeted with one of the hidden gems of Puget Sound. This is a beautiful state park with hiking trails, cool history and about a mile of shoreline to explore.

Maury Island Marine Park

Another great beach access that takes some effort to get to. There is about 2 miles of shore to hunt along the southern end of Maury Island. It's a good hike down to the beach, probably 3/4 of a mile with a decent grade. Few people make the effort. Visit during the off-season and you're likely to have the beach to yourself.

10. Olympia Area

Sequalitchew Creek Beach

This is a popular 1.5 mile trail (3 mile round-trip from the trailhead to the beach). The trailhead starts in Dupont adjacent to the Dupont City Police Department. Take the well-maintained trail that follows along the creek. The path is smooth and it is a fairly easy hike.

Burfoot Park

Burfoot Park provides a beautiful beach access about 15 minutes north of Olympia. The trail down from the main parking area is less than 1/4 mile and an easy hike. There's a nice rocky beach with sandy cliffs as a backdrop. Lots of colorful rocks, shells, and fun sea creatures are abundant at this site. There's a nice view of the State Capital from the beach.

Harstine Island State Park

This is a wonderful beach access on Harstine Island. It's a bit out of the way, which means it gets less pressure from rockhounds and other visitors. The hike from the parking area down to the beach takes some efforts. The trail is well-maintained, but there's enough elevation drop that you will definitely break a sweat on the hike back out. I have had the beach to myself anytime I have visited. There is a mix of sand and gravel shoreline.

11. Port Townsend

North Beach County Park

Fort Worden HSP

Fort Casey

Panorama Vista CP

Port Townsend

Point No Point

Map Data ©2023 Google

Point No Point

The north-facing beach at Point No Point is usually all sand, but venture around the bend to the east-facing beach and it usually has a lot more gravel. This can be a great site to find agates, and there's no shortage of good driftwood here also.

Fort Warden Historic State Park

Fort Warden is a 432-acre multi-use park with more than 2 miles of saltwater shoreline and a wide variety of services and facilities. You can definitely find some nice agates and jaspers here, but sea glass is the prize here. If you want to pass on paying the parking fee, go visit the nearby North Beach County Park on the west side of Fort Warden Park.

North Beach County Park

If you are looking for the best sea glass hunting site in the Pacific Northwest, then North Beach is the place for you. Up until the 1960s, this was the location of a county dump, where garbage was dumped directly into the water and forgotten. Fortunately we are a tad more environmentally conscious today. One benefit of this dumping was that now there is an abundance of waterworn sea glass that washes ashore in this area.

Glass can be found in a wide array of colors. Most serious sea glass hunters are here for the rich reds and deep blues. Brown and green glass is common. Most pieces are frosty and waterworn into little glass "pebbles" that are popular to use in jewelry.

You can take a good hike from the parking lot at the park and head west, for about 2.7 miles toward McCurdy Point. The beach is quite narrow here, so you should arrive around high tide and start your hike when the tide is receding.

Panorama Vista County Park

This is a nice free county park access on the west side of Miller Peninsula State Park. You can hike west toward Travis Spit and Klapot Point for about 3 miles. You can find agates and a lot of beautiful rocks at this site that is overlooked by a lot of people.

12. Strait of Juan de Fuca

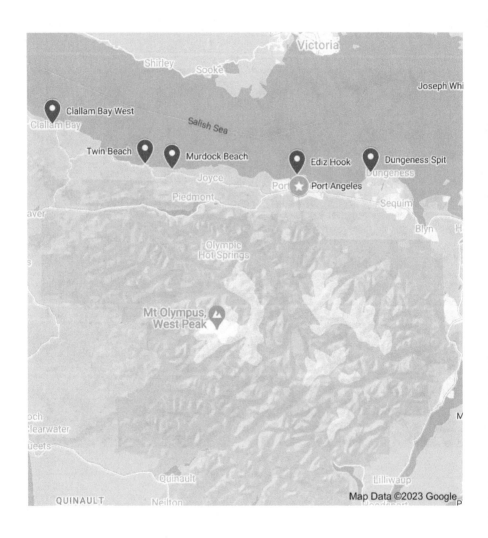

Dungeness Recreation Area

The Dungeness Recreation Area is adjacent to the Dungeness Spit, the longest sand spit in the United States. It is located about 15 miles east of Port Angeles. This natural wonder juts out into the Strait of Juan de Fuca for approximately 5 miles. You will find a mixture of expansive sandy areas with many gravel beds as well. A popular hike is to venture out toward the north end of the spit and see the lighthouse.

Ediz Hook

This is another long sand spit that extends out onto the Strait of Juan de Fuca. This is a popular site due to the close proximity to Port Angeles. I found a lot of modern glass here, but a few pieces of nice frosted sea glass. A few jaspers and other interesting rocks to bring home and tumble too.

Murdock Beach

This beach is a well-kept secret among Washington rockhounds. It is about 22 miles west of Port Angeles. Not only are there a wide array of agates, jasper and other minerals, but there are also abundant fossils on this beach too. Murdock Beach has lots of concretions, which are round balls of rock that form around fossil fragments.

Crack open these round concretions to reveal the treasures inside. Often they are empty. Others will have very small fragments of shells or other ancient marine fossils. A complete fossil shell or clam is a real prize, and even intact crab fossils have been found on Murdock Beach. Cracking open these concretions and exposing complete fossils takes practice and a lot of patience.

Twin Beach

This is a small beach access about 28 miles west of Port Angeles. The main access is on the east side of the West Twin River bridge. Pull down from the main road to the small parking area. Search the wide gravel beds at the mouth of the river. Another access is to drive across the bridge and park at the wide pullout off the highway just west of the bridge to access the beach on the west side of the river.

Clallam Bay (West)

The main access point in Clallam Bay has a broken bridge that prevents access to the beach. To get to the gravel beach, continue driving west on Highway 112 through Clallam Bay and look for the "Clallam Bay West" access on the edge of town. This is a wonderful beach great for rockhounding. It is quite a ways from any large town, so there usually isn't a lot of rockhounding pressure aside from a few locals.

13. La Push

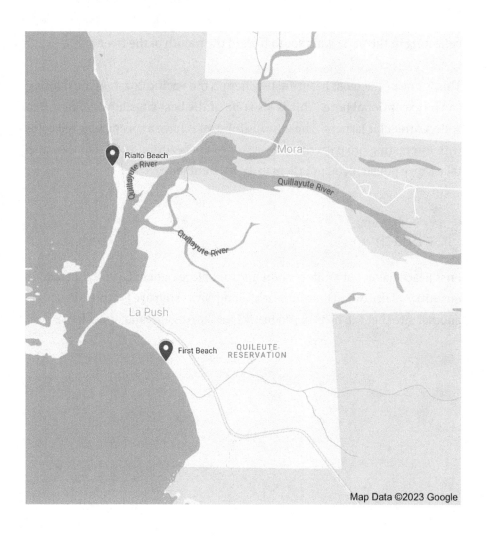

Map Data ©2023 Google

Both of these beaches are on the Quileute Indian Reservation. Rockhounds have hunted these beaches for years and I have never heard of any issues with collecting modest quantities of rocks at either of these beaches.

Rialto Beach

This rock strewn beach at the mouth of the Quillayute River is one of the top destinations for Washington rockhounds. The main parking area is at the border of the reservation and Olympic National Park. If you want to avoid collecting in the park, walk south toward the mouth of the river.

This is one of the most beautiful beaches on the Pacific Coast. Agate hunting can be exceptional here. This is also one of the best sites in Washington to collect orbicular jaspers. These beautiful stones have a spectacular red color with interesting orb patterns. These stones are beautiful as-is, but they also take a nice polish if you put them in a rock tumbler.

First Beach

First Beach has about 1 mile of shoreline to explore right in La Push. Incredible quantities of driftwood line the beach, along with extensive gravel beds. This is another site that can be very productive for both agates and orbicular jaspers.

14. Olympic National Park

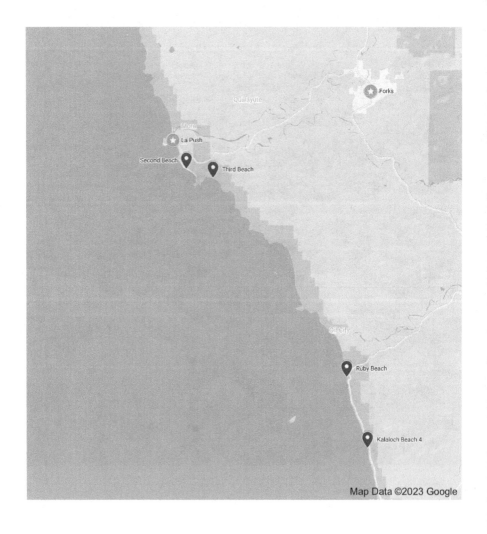

There are many miles of beautiful rocky beaches along the Pacific Coast that are within the Olympic National Park. Rockhounding within the park is prohibited. Casual collecting of a few stones has never been heavily enforced to my knowledge, but for the purposes of this book these beaches are listed for informational purposes only.

Shi Shi Beach

There is about a 2 mile hike to get to Shi Shi Beach. In addition to the Wilderness permit needed to access the park, you will also need to get a Makah Reservation Pass since the trailhead and most of the trail is on the reservation.

Second Beach

Second Beach is accessible by a trailhead about 1 mile before you reach La Push. The trail to get to the beach is about a 1/2 mile hike.

Third Beach

The trailhead to Third Beach is roughly 2.5 miles east of La Push, off of La Push Road. The trail is 1.3 miles with a small decent down to the beach.

Ruby Beach

Ruby Beach is very popular and easily accessible from Highway 101, about 27 miles south of Forks. The trail down to the beach from the parking area is relatively short (~0.25 miles), but its a fairly good drop to get down there. The hike will be worth it, with amble rocky shores to explore and beautiful sea stacks that make this one of Washington's most beautiful beaches.

Kolaloch Beach 4

Another lovely beach to do some beachcombing and explore. From this access you can walk miles and miles in both direction. You'll have millions of pebbles and stones to see. The hike from the parking lot is short, but it's a fairly steep drop down to the beach.

15. Ocean Shores

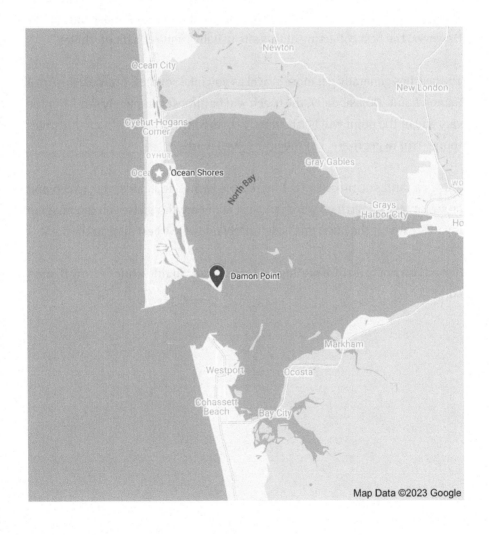

Damon Point

There are plenty of beaches that you can explore near Ocean Shores, but if you're here for beachcombing and rockhounding, then Damon Point is the only site worth mentioning. It is far and away the best places to hunt for rocks in the area, and easily one of the best sites on the Washington Coast.

Damon Point is a point of land that extends out into the north end of Grays Harbor. The beach is easily accessible from the parking area and there's a decent change that you will start finding good material almost right away. However, the best collecting at this site usually requires a bit of a hike.

The beaches generally get more gravel as you hike southeast toward the tip of Damon Point. Occasionally, the beach will be almost completely sand, but the very end of the point will be absolutely covered with rocks. It's about 4 miles round-trip to get there, but the hike is well worth it.

This is a fantastic place to find incredible carnelian agates, red, green and orbicular jasper, petrified wood, and just about anything else you can imagine. If you are up for the hike, this is definitely one of the best sites in the book.

Be cautious not to disturb nesting birds and other wildlife while visiting Damon Point.

16. Oceanside

The beaches near the town of Oceanside have long been known for producing nice agates and jaspers. Also be on the lookout for zeolites, a group of naturally occurring, crystalline minerals that are primarily composed of silicon, oxygen and water with trace amounts of calcium, sodium and potassium. Look for rounded basalt boulders with small air pockets filled with tiny white and green crystals. They are commonly found at all three of the beaches listed below.

Short Beach

This beautiful beach feels isolated from the world. It is located about a mile north of Oceanside. Take the Cape Meares Loop Road (now closed and no longer a loop) and keep an eye out for wide pullout beside a chain link fence and the sign marking the trailhead. The hike is relatively short, but it's quite a drop from the road getting down to the beach.

This has become a very popular beach in recent years. There can be good rocks present on the beach throughout the year, even during the summer.

Tunnel Beach

As far as I know, this is the only beach on the Pacific Coast that you get to by traversing a 100' tunnel bored through solid rock. The tunnel was built in 1926 by resort owners to allow guests access to more beachfront. Find the tunnel entrance by walking north along the beach at Oceanside. Bring a flashlight and good footwear.

Tunnel beach is a reliable agate hunting beach. Most commonly you can expect to find small clear and pale yellow agates at the beaches in the Oceanside area.

Oceanside Beach State Park

Park at the Oceanside Beach State Recreation Site for easy access to this beach. Usually the best gravel beds are found to the north, up against the cliffs. Bring a flashlight with you so you can check out Tunnel Beach also while you are here.

17. Lincoln City

In addition to the great rockhounding opportunities, there is also a neat opportunity to find ornamental glass floats on the beaches of Lincoln City. An annual event called "Finder's Keeper's" is sponsored by the town. Periodically throughout the year, volunteers hide beautiful glass floats on the beach for visitors to find. Look for them above the high tide line, below the beach embankment. Usually they are carefully tucked in among the driftwood or tall beach grasses.

Roads End State Recreation Site

The presence of cobble material at Roads End can be hit-or-miss depending on the tides (just like any beach on the Oregon Coast). If you only see sand from the parking lot, all is not lost! The real hidden gem at Roads End is a small beach about 1 mile north of the main parking lot. Walk north toward the rocky point known as "God's Thumb." At low tide, you can scramble around the large basalt rocks and access a small hidden beach that usually has some excellent rockhounding. This is a particularly good spot to check if other beaches are all sanded up.

Nelscott Beach

This beach on the southern end of Lincoln City provides visitors a good opportunity to find agates. The parking area is small and it can fill up quickly on weekends. This site is very accessible with parking right on the beach.

Taft Waterfront Park

Some of my best days agate hunting in Lincoln City has been at Taft. This is probably the most popular beach in the area for agates and glass floats. There is a large parking area, restrooms, and accessibility is good. Look for Finders

Keepers glass floats among the driftwood. Walk the beach along the north end of Siletz Bay and look for other rockhounders. If there are agates out, there will undoubtedly be other folks out looking at this site.

18. Depoe Bay

Fogarty Creek State Recreation Area

Fogarty Beach is located about 3 miles north of Depoe Bay. You park on the east side of the road and take a path that follows the creek under Highway 101. As you approach the beach and look out toward the Pacific Ocean you will see a large rock cliff that extend out into the ocean separating two beaches.

The beach south of the rocks almost always has an assortment of rocks, mostly smaller pebbles. This is a very reliable place to find small agates, jaspers, and even the occasional fossil specimen.

Beverly Beach State Park

This is probably the best spot on the Oregon Coast to find marine fossils. An ancient seafloor of sandstone and shales known as the Astoria Formation is exposed here that has preserved a wide array of clams, scallops, snails and other marine fossils. These fossils erode and wash up on the beach.

They are most commonly found in a 15-20 mile stretch of beach around Newport, starting at Devil's Punchbowl at the north down to Ona Beach to the south. For fossil hunters, Beverly Beach and Moolack Beach are two great spots to explore. Even when the beaches are sandy in the summer, you can sometimes look up high on the beach and still find nice specimens.

19. Newport

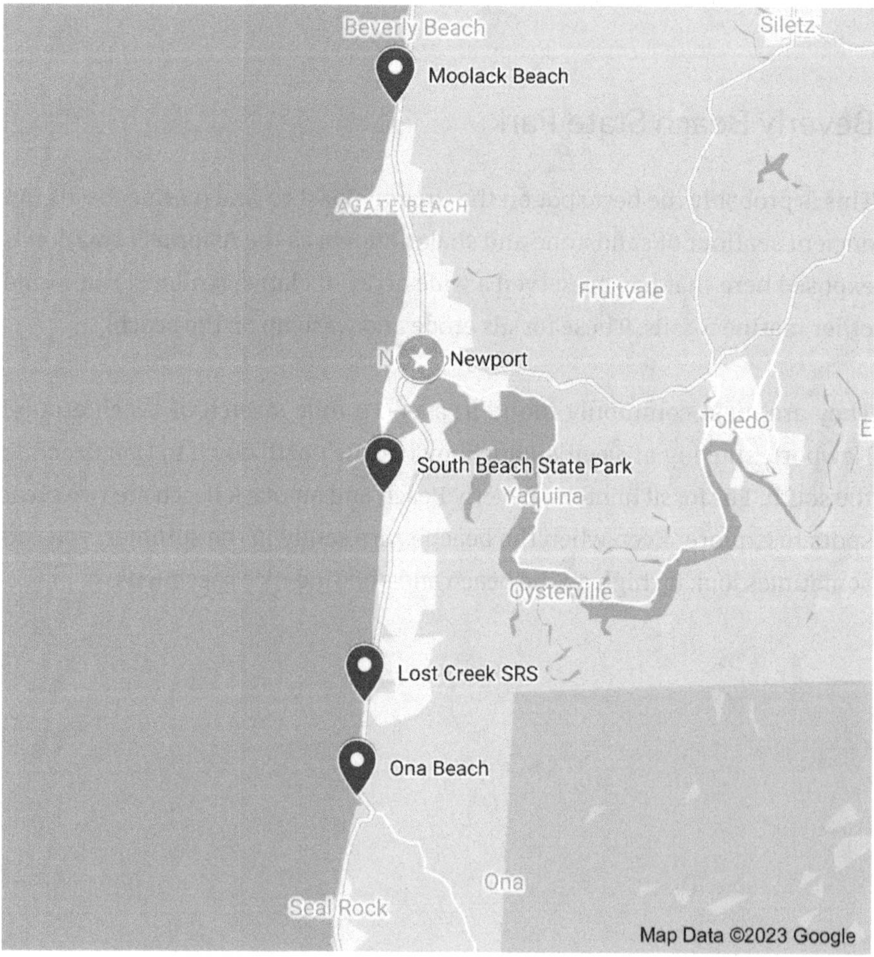

Beverly Beach
Siletz
Moolack Beach
AGATE BEACH
Fruitvale
Newport
Toledo
South Beach State Park
Yaquina
Oysterville
Lost Creek SRS
Ona Beach
Ona
Seal Rock
Map Data ©2023 Google

Moolack Beach

Look for a large pullout on the west side of Highway 101, about 4.5 miles north of Newport. This access is basically the same long sandy beach that extends from Devil's Punchbowl down to Yaquina Head. The Moolack Beach access is a great spot to find agates and jaspers when there is gravel to search. Most of the time it has sand and hunting is difficult. Your success will be largely dependent on the tides and the weather exposing the gravel beds. Fossils are present here and commonly found. Invertebrate fossils (plants and animals with no backbone) can be kept, but Oregon law states that vertebrate fossils (bones from fish and marine mammals) cannot be kept.

South Beach State Park

This is another great site for rockhounding just south of Yaquina Bay in Newport. Park at the day-use parking area and hike over the sand hill to the beach. Good agate hunting can be found starting at the south jetty and extending south for many miles. Any patch of exposed rocks is worth your time to explore.

In addition to the typical clear/yellow/orange colored agates, also be on the lookout for the less common clear/blue/black agates. These can be found throughout the Newport area. They can be tricky to see, since they blend in quite well with the millions of black stones that are present on the beach. When in doubt, pick them up and see if you can shine a light through them. Black agates are a real prize and highly valued by collectors.

Lost Creek State Recreation Site

Another beach to hunt for the elusive "Newport Blue" agates is at Lost Creek Beach. The main parking area is about 7 miles south of Newport. There is also a small parking pullout (only large enough for about 4 vehicles) that is about 5.5 miles south of Newport, just past the airport. Both accesses are great spots to hit the beach in search of both agates and fossils.

Ona Beach

Ona Beach is about 8 miles south of Newport. There is a small gravel parking area as the highway begins to bend, or there is a large paved parking lot with a bathroom right before the Highway 101 crosses Beaver Creek.

This is the southern extent of the Astoria Formation and you can still find plenty of fossils on Ona Beach. I've never had much luck finding agates or jaspers here, but I'm sure this would be a good place to look if you time it right.

20. Yachats

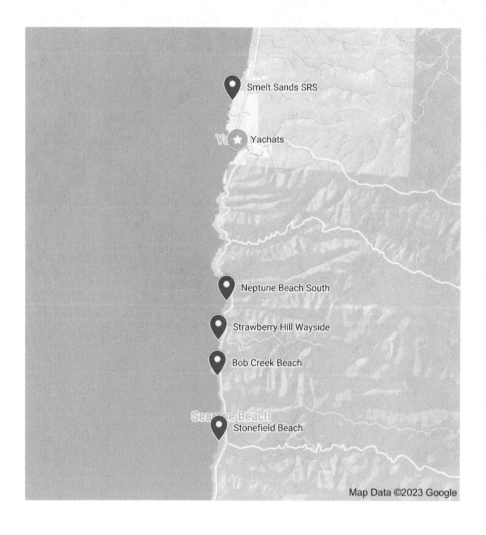

Smelt Sands State Recreation Site

The Smelt Sands access is on the north end of town just as you entering Yachats. Yachats has a rugged rocky shoreline that is famous for producing some incredible crashing waves during winter storms. This area is beautiful, but also dangerous. Use caution when exploring these beaches.

While most of the jagged shoreline is unsuitable for rockhounding, there are a few small beaches and narrow pockets of sand between the basalt rocks where you are almost guaranteed to find agates. The best spot is right in front of the parking area, slightly to the left as you walk toward the beach. The gravel here is usually pea-sized and the agates are similar in size.

Neptune Beach

There are two primary access points to Neptune Beach. One is at the Neptune State Scenic Viewpoint, the other is Neptune Beach South. Both are great locations to search for central Oregon Coast agates. As with all beaches south of Yachats, you have a very good chance of finding some nice agates here. If the beach is sanded up, try going to Neptune Beach South and hunting the rocks at the mouth of Cummins Creek where it flows onto the beach.

Strawberry Hill Wayside

This is one of my favorite sites in this book. Not only does this beach consistently produce agates, but I have also found some very large ones here. Some of my best pieces were found at Strawberry Hill. Getting down to the beach from the parking area is a bit of a scramble down a trail and over some cliffy rocks, so this site won't be for everyone. This parking area is also quite small and can fill up quickly during the busy season.

Bob Creek Beach

Bob Creek is truly a "hidden gem" on the coast. It is about 9 miles south of Yachats. The parking lot is very small, but there is some additional parking at the wide spot on the east side of the highway. Beautiful tide pools filled with starfish, anemones, mussels, crabs and other sea life abound.

This is a long rocky beach about 1/2 mile long. There can be gravel present year-round, and the agate hunting at this site is excellent.

Stonefield Beach

Stonefield is another of Yachats' famous agate hunting beaches. There is parking on both sides of the bridge over Tenmile Creek. Personally I would recommend the north side parking lot because it is larger and less secluded. Unfortunately, break-ins have become more common on the Oregon Coast in recent years, and Stonefield Beach has gotten particularly bad.

21. Charleston

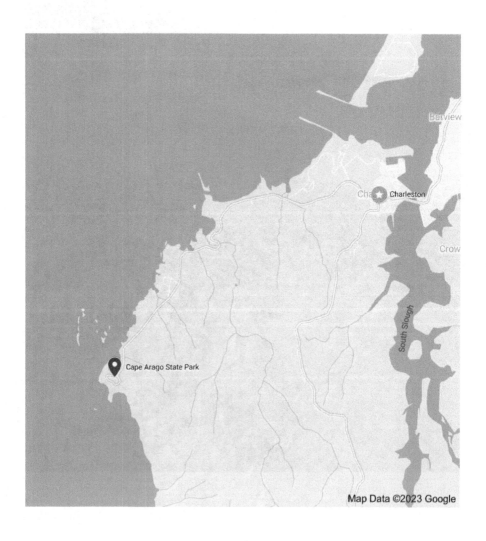

The rocky shorelines around Charleston are excellent places to look for agates and jaspers. The best stretch for rockhounding are the beaches along the Cape Arago Highway, from Charleston to Cape Arago. There are a few others that require treacherous hikes to get down to the beach, but they can also be great spots to look. Bastendorff Beach, Lighthouse Beach and Sunset Bay can all produce agates from time to time, but usually they are mostly sand. I have had the best luck at Cape Arago.

Cape Arago State Park

The Cape Arago Highway dead ends up high on Cape Arago. To get down to the beach on the south side you will have to take a short hike on the Cape Arago South Cove Trail. It's a short, steep path down to the beach. Nice tide pools and some sandy sections with more rocky stretches further south.

You can also take a north trail as well, but it is closed seasonally from March 1 to June 30 to protect sea lion pups. The reef complex at nearby Simpson Reef and Shell Island can be home to several thousand sea lions at any given time. Bring your binoculars if you visit, this is one of the best places for viewing marine mammals anywhere on the coast.

22. Bandon

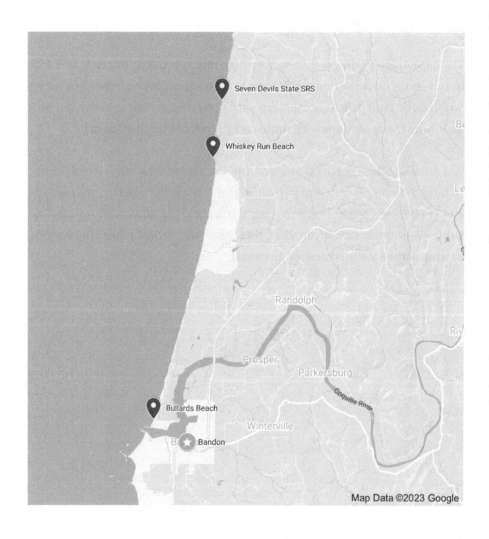

Seven Devils State Recreation Site

This is a known site for agate hunting and also an excellent spot to collect driftwood. You can hike north on the beach for several miles and have a good change finding some good stuff if the gravels are exposed.

It's worth noting that all Oregon Coast beaches are public land, but the access to those beaches is not necessarily guaranteed. Some access point that have been used by locals for years off of Seven Devils Road have recently been blocked off by private landowners... this does NOT mean that the beach is private, only the land where people were accessing the beach. You can hike north from the Seven Devils State Recreation Site and legally access both Agate Beach and Sacchi Beach, which are both excellent spots to hunt for agates as well.

Whiskey Run Beach

One of the few beaches on the Oregon Coast that you are allowed to drive on. An excellent option if mobility is an issue. Just don't get stuck in the sand!

Bullards Beach

This is a favorite hunting site for rockhounds in the Bandon area. Gravel beds are commonly exposed on the beach near the Coquille River Lighthouse. On a good day, there can be miles of gravel to explore. Plenty of agates, jaspers and other cool rocks. This is also a fairly reliable place to find petrified wood. It can take trained eye to spot them, so take it slow.

23. Port Orford

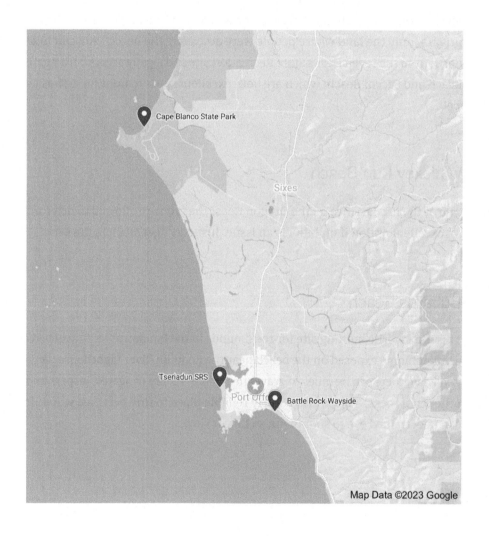

Cape Blanco State Park

Sixes

Tseriadun SRS

Port Orford

Battle Rock Wayside

Map Data ©2023 Google

Cape Blanco State Park

There are miles and miles of beach to explore north and south of Cape Blanco. You can drive up to the lighthouse and hike down the hill to the north beach, or you can park at the Hughes Historic House and take the trail that follows down the Sixes River all the way to the beach. This takes more effort to get to but there are less people. Another access is to the beach south of Cape Blanco. Take the campground loop around and look for the sign directing you to the beach. The road is narrow and steep, but it will take you down close to the south beach.

Tseriadun State Recreation Site

This is a fantastic rockhounding spot directly west of Port Orford. You'll find lots of tiny rocks on this beach with plenty of agates mixed in. I'm not sure when it got the name "Tseriadun," but most locals still call this Agate Beach. You can walk north for many miles. There is another access a few miles north of here called Paradise Point Recreation area, but I've had the best luck on the south end closer to the cliffs at The Heads.

Battle Rock Wayside

Sometime the rockhounding can be pretty good right in Port Orford at the Battle Rock Wayside located right where Highway 101 turns through town. Quite a few people hunt the beach right by the wayside, but most don't hike the beach south very far. There is a long, 5-mile section of the coast between Battle Rock and Humbug Mountain that gets very little pressure from the public. There are a few small pullouts, but no major access points in this section. If you take the extra effort to find these spots, it can definitely pay off with some tremendous beachcombing.

24. Gold Beach

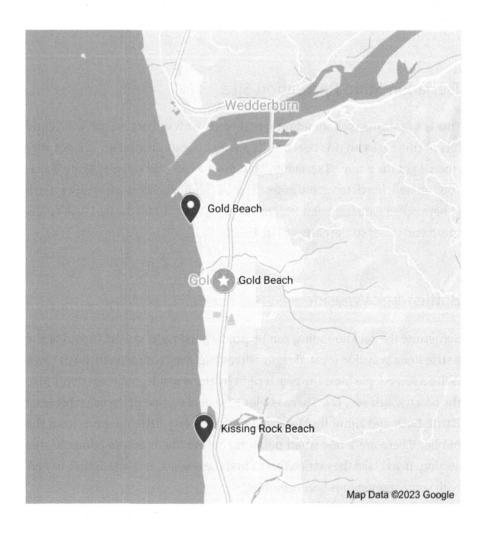

Gold Beach

The mighty Rogue River provides a ready supply of neat rocks that get deposited along the beach at Gold Beach. Agates and jaspers are plentiful when the gravel beds are exposed. Hunt around the north jetty by taking the bridge over the Rogue River and immediately turning left on Wedderburn Loop. Gravel beds will often accumulate adjacent next to the jetty, but you can have luck north all the way to Otter Point.

The beaches right in town are good as well, from the south jetty right on south. There are many accesses to the beach right in town.

Gold Beach also hides glass floats on the beach from February to April to promote tourism. You can keep the floats that you find, and some of them even have tags that you can bring to the Visitors Center for additional prizes.

Kissing Rock

There is a good beach access about 2 miles south of Gold Beach that consistently has good gravel, often better than what you can find in town. Kissing Rock is a unique rock formation that is hard to miss as you are heading down the highway. There's a large parking area and access to the beach is easy.

25. Brookings

Brookings has beautiful cliff shorelines will nice little rocky beaches tucked in. There are lots of good beaches to explore that have good rockhounding.

You can also explore the Chetco River, which flows into the Pacific Ocean at Brookings. Take the road that follows upriver and visit Loeb State Park. Go a bit further inland and you will be on Forest Service land with miles of riverbank to explore.

McVay Rock State Recreation Site

There are lots of good beach access points near Brookings, but I have found the most productive for rockhounding to be at McVay Rock. It is about 4 miles south of town. The beach is a nice gravely beach with lots to offer.

Lots of pretty little stones with plenty of agates, jasper, and other interesting colorful rocks mixed in. There are usually a few pieces of colored sea glass to find here as well.

Crissey Field Recreation Site

About 6 miles south of Brooking, immediately before you reach the California border is the access to Crissey Field. This beach can be hit-or-miss and will often have only sand, but occasionally you will find some exposed gravel to search. Not nearly as productive as McVay Rock but still worth checking, especially around the mouth of Winchuck River.

26. Crescent City

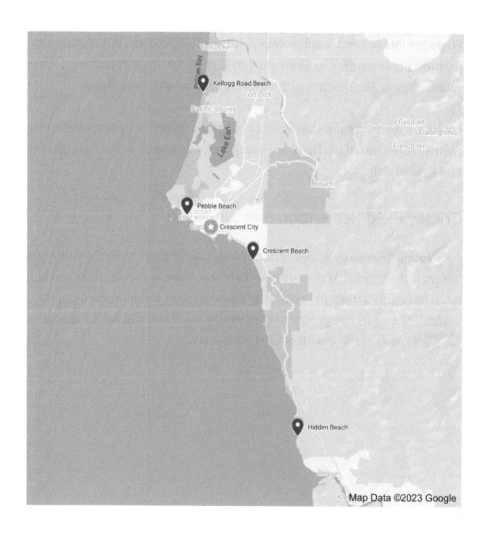

Map Data ©2023 Google

The beaches of Del Norte County are probably the best place to find agates on the California Coast. The agates here can have an incredible variety of colors and patterns. Two main rivers, the Smith River and the Klamath River, drain into the Pacific Ocean here, bringing a steady supply of new material to the nearby beaches.

Kellogg Road Beach

Located about 11 miles north of Crescent City and adjacent to Tolowa Dunes State Park. A less-crowded option that some other beaches in the area. You can drive on this beach, so its definitely a good option for folks with mobility issues. Plenty of agates, seashells and sand dollars.

Pebble Beach

This one is a great beach right in Crescent City. There are several parking areas off of Pebble Beach Road that provide easy access to the shoreline. Continue up the road past the airport and look for the trailhead to Point St. George. Several miles of beach to investigate.

Crescent Beach

There are several good access points to Crescent Beach. There's a large parking area about 2.5 miles south of Crescent City right where Highway 101 starts to leave the coastline. There are also several trails from Enderts Beach Road that you can take to the beach. There's about 4 miles of beach between Whaler Island and the Crescent Beach overlook that you can hunt.

Hidden Beach

Look for a trailhead that starts inconspicuously right off of Highway 101, across from Trees of Mystery on the west end of the parking lot for the motel. The trail crosses a small creek and eventually ties in with the Coastal Trail. A small trail drops down to a beach right there, or you can go south on the coastal trail for another 1/2 miles and access another rocky beach.

The hike is a little less 2 miles roundtrip. This is a great beach if you are looking for some solitude, it doesn't get a lot of visitors.

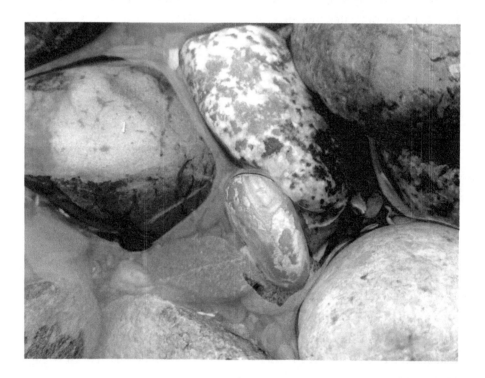

27. Trinidad

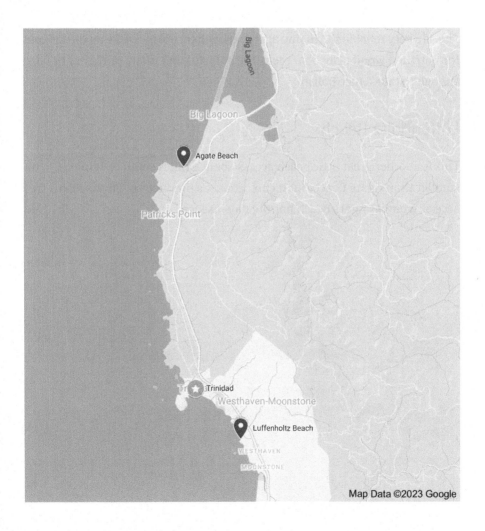

Agate Beach

You know when a place is called "Agate Beach," you've probably found a good place to do some beachcombing! Drive north of Trinidad on Highway 101 for about 7 miles. Currently has an $8 day use fee. This is a beautiful beach covered with polished stones.

Access the beach from Sue Meg State Park, and take a short but steep trail down to the beach.

This is a very reliable site to find agates and other cool rocks. Be on the lookout for petrified wood also. The rocks are colorful and many of them are hard enough to take a nice polish.

Luffenholtz Beach

This is another great little beach access about 2 miles south of Trinidad. A bit smaller than Agate Beach but it can be just as productive. This is also a free access, whereas Agate Beach has the day-use fee.

28. Fort Bragg

This final chapter contains a site that is one of the most popular destinations for beachcombers on the entire Pacific Coast...

Glass Beach

Glass beach was created from years of garbage and waste dumping at several locations around Fort Bragg from 1906 to as recently as 1967. The glass from all sorts of waste eventually broke and eroded into smooth glass pebbles.

Today, there are several beaches around Fort Bragg that have accumulated incredible amounts of sea glass that cover the beach. Locals will tell you that decades of collecting has diminished the amount of glass, and its not nearly as abundant as it was years ago. It may not be the solid blankets of glass that were there decades ago, but there is still an incredible amount of sea glass in a wide array of colors. Of course, storms and tides effect the concentration of glass on the beach as well.

There is a large parking area at the trailhead to Glass Beach off of Noyo Point Road on the northern end of Fort Bragg. Take a short trail down the beach.

Note that collecting of glass is no longer allowed. Kind of unusual that it is considered a "natural resource" since the glass is technically garbage, but I do understand the uniqueness of the beach, and how much it will change over time if everyone takes the glass.

Made in the USA
Las Vegas, NV
13 January 2024